MEET THE CROODS

Popcorn ELT Readers

New Words

adventure

This is an **adventure**.

cave

This is a **cave**.

afraid

The boy is **afraid**.

dangerous

This animal is **dangerous**.

family

This is a **family**.

fire

This is a **fire**.

strong

The man is **strong**.

Where's the popcorn?
Look in your book.
Can you find it?

MEET THE CROODS

My name is Eep. I live in a **cave** with my **family**.

Eep

I do not like the **cave**. It is dark.
I like to be in the sun.

Grug

This is my dad. His name is Grug.
He is tall and **strong**.

This is my mum.
Her name is Ugga.
She has got brown hair.

Ugga

Gran

This is Gran. She is very old.
Sometimes she is angry with Grug.

My brother is nine years old.
His name is Thunk.

Thunk

Sandy

My sister Sandy is very small.
She does not speak.

At night we go in the **cave**.

'You can't go out of the **cave** at night,'
my dad says. 'It's **dangerous**.'

In the morning, we always want food.
'We're hungry,' we say.

We look for food but there are **dangerous** animals. We run away.

Douglas

Some animals are very nice. This is
Douglas. He is our friend.

One day, we meet Guy. Now he is my friend.

Guy

Guy can make a **fire**. Now we can see when it is dark.

'Come out of the **cave**,' Guy says.
'Come out in the sun.'

We are not **afraid** now.

We want to have an **adventure**!

After you read

1 Match the pictures with the sentences.

a)

i) The cave is dark.

b)

ii) She has got brown hair.

c)

iii) They are friends.

d)

iv) The fire is hot.

e)

v) They are afraid.

2 Look at the pictures and complete the words.

a) This animal is
d <u>a</u> n <u>g</u> e <u>r</u> o <u>u</u> s

b) Douglas is   n __ c __

c) Grug is   a __ g __ y

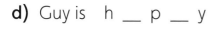

d) Guy is   h __ p __ y

e) Gran is   o __ d

f) Sandy is   s m __ l __

3 a Look at the pictures and complete the words.

mum   dad   brother   sister

My family

....

....

....

me

....

b Draw a picture of your family.

Quiz time!

Read the sentences. Answer Yes or No.

		Yes	No
1)	Eep likes caves.	☐	☐
2)	Gran has got white hair.	☐	☐
3)	Thunk is ten years old.	☐	☐
4)	Grug does not speak.	☐	☐
5)	Sandy is Guy's sister.	☐	☐

SCORES

How many of your answers are correct?

0–2: Read the book again! Can you answer the questions now?

3–4: Good work! The Croods like you!

5: Wow! Are you a Crood?

Chant

1 🎵 **Listen and read.**

Guy's Chant

I'm not afraid of the dark.
I've got fire in my hand.
Now I can see,
Now I understand.

The sun comes again.
The night goes away.
Now I can see,
It's a happy day.

2 🎵 **Say the chant.**